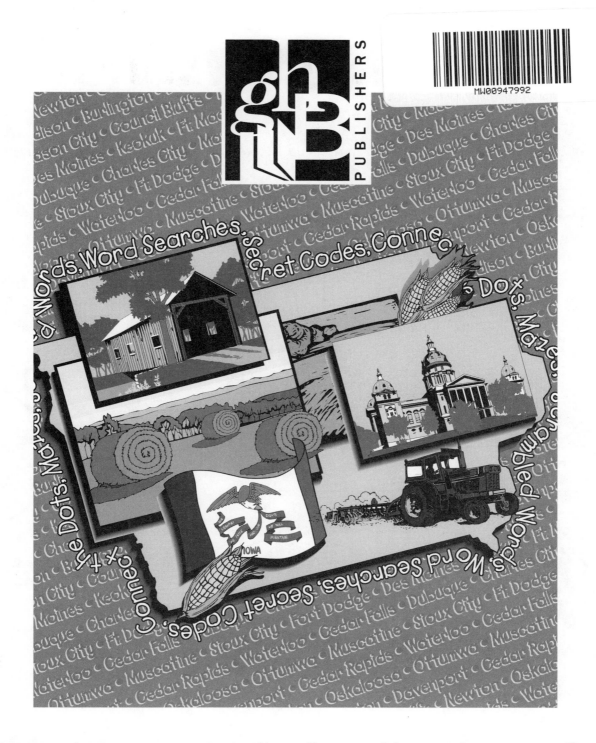

Written by Mary Ann Gensicke • Illustrated by Sandra Ure Griffin

Copyright © 2001 by GHB Publishers, L.L.C.
Illustrations (except pp. 16, 35) © 2001 by Sandra Ure Griffin
Illustrations pp. 16, 35   by Amy Nicole Wilson

Cover design by Grey Communications

Printed in the United States of America by Plus Communications, St. Louis
05 04 03 02 01 00   10 9 8 7 6 5 4 3 2 1

STATE SYMBOLS

Iowa has six state symbols. They are listed here. Write each name below its picture.

State flag
Wild rose, the state flower
Geode, the state rock
Great seal of the state of Iowa
Oak, the state tree
Eastern goldfinch, the state bird

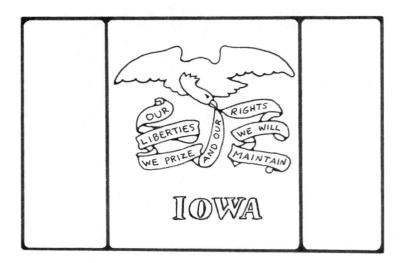

_____

_____

_____

_____

Iowa Is Everywhere

Work this puzzle to see how many times you can find the word IOWA. Check across, down, backward, and at an angle. Draw a line through each one you find.

How many did you find? _____

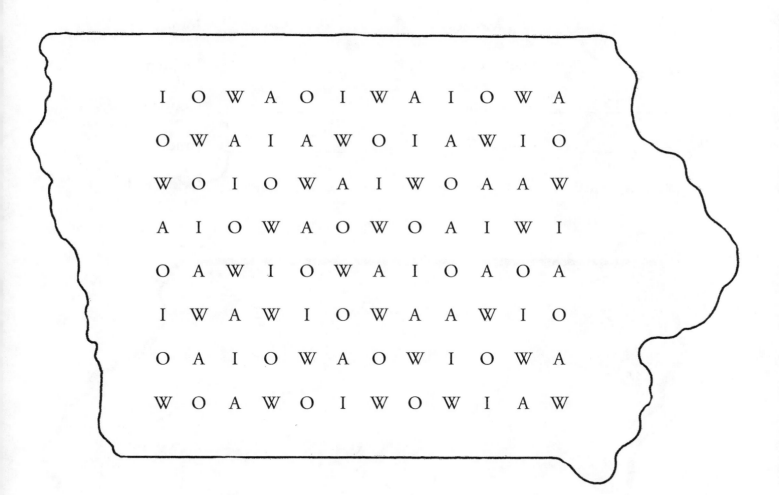

I O W A O I W A I O W A

O W A I A W O I A W I O

W O I O W A I W O A A W

A I O W A O W O A I W I

O A W I O W A I O A O A

I W A W I O W A A W I O

O A I O W A O W I O W A

W O A W O I W O W I A W

Largest Cities

The largest cities in Iowa are Des Moines, Cedar Rapids, Davenport, Sioux City, Waterloo, Iowa City, Dubuque, Council Bluffs, Ames, and Cedar Falls.

Can you find them on the map? Write the number of each city on the line in front of its name.

_____ Des Moines   _____ Iowa City

_____ Cedar Rapids   _____ Dubuque

_____ Davenport   _____ Council Bluffs

_____ Sioux City   _____ Ames

_____ Waterloo   _____ Cedar Falls

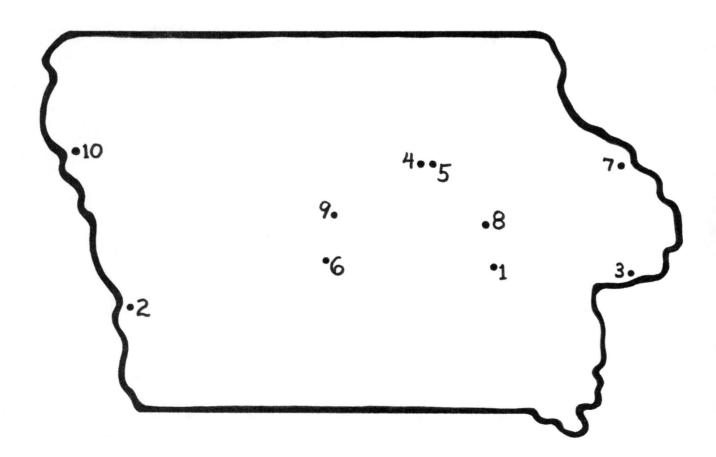

STATEHOOD

Color all the spaces that have a dot in them.
You will find the year that Iowa became a state.

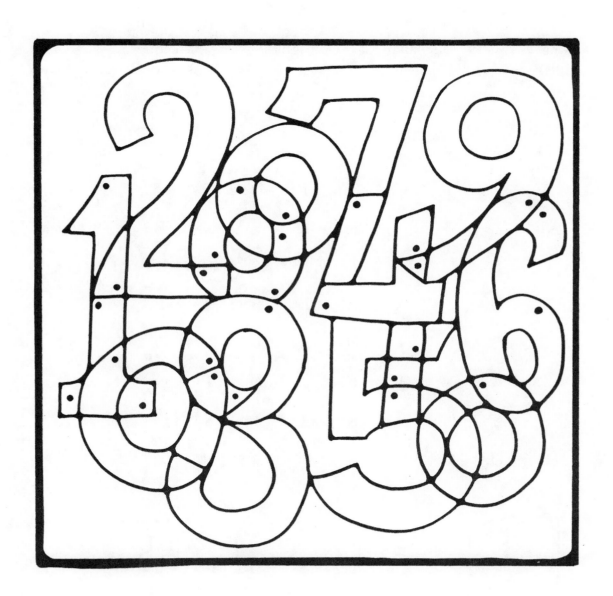

Ninety-Nine Counties

Iowa has many counties. Find these Iowa counties in the puzzle below. Look across, down, and at an angle to find them.

Tama	Buchanan	Wright	Osceola	Union
Mills	Harrison	Warren	Bremer	Davis
Scott	Lucas	Sac	Clay	

```
D  A  V  I  S  U  T  A  M  A  S
W  R  I  G  H  T  D  C  W  R  O
S  I  W  A  R  R  E  N  E  C  S
C  L  M  I  L  L  S  M  R  L  C
O  U  S  A  C  E  E  A  P  A  E
T  C  R  T  U  R  L  L  D  Y  O
T  A  X  J  B  U  N  I  O  N  L
R  S  H  A  R  R  I  S  O  N  A
B  U  C  H  A  N  A  N  Z  I  L
```

WARREN

SCOTT

BUCHANAN

HARRISON

SAC

MILLS

6

Iowa's John Wayne

John Wayne was a famous actor in western movies. He was born in
Winterset. He won an Academy Award for his work in the film
True Grit. People can visit the house where he was born.

In the design below, color all the shapes that have a W in
them. Then you will see John Wayne's nickname.

Iowa Fun Facts

Interesting people and places are part of Iowa and its history. For example, the famous opera singer Simon Estes was born in Centerville. Estes graduated from the University of Iowa and then studied opera at the Juilliard School of Music.

Carrie Chapman Catt was a Mason City educator who helped women get the right to vote in 1920. She graduated from Iowa State College.

Osceola County has the highest point in Iowa, at 1,670 feet.

East Okoboji is 16 miles long. It is the longest natural lake in the state.

West Okoboji is one of the three lakes that have the bluest water in the world. It is the deepest natural lake in the state, at 136 feet.

Iowa's largest county in square miles is Kossuth County.

Eskimo Pie, a popular ice-cream treat, was invented in Onawa by Christian Nelson in 1920.

Sac County, the popcorn capital of the world, created a popcorn ball 22 feet around that weighed more than a ton.

Hamburgers were first served in Iowa at Clarinda. The dish was suggested to a restaurant owner by his friend, a butcher, who probably was from Germany. Most Germans who came to live in the United States left Germany through the port of Hamburg.

An Iowa Composer

Meredith Willson was born and raised in Mason City. He played the flute and the piccolo in high school. When he grew up, he wrote a famous musical called *The Music Man*. One of the songs from it is "76 _____ ."

Connect the dots to see the musical instrument from the title of this famous song.

4-H Clubs in Iowa

A teacher in Iowa, Jessie Schambaugh, helped start after-school clubs for young children. The clubs taught things the children needed to know when they grew up, especially if they were going to be farmers. Schambaugh was one of many people across the United States who worked to create clubs like this. After a while, the groups were called 4-H clubs. The four H's stand for head, heart, hands, and health.

Can you find four H's in the fair scenes below?

Iowa Artist Grant Wood

The painter Grant Wood created a colorful patterned floor in his art studio at Cedar Rapids. He marked shapes on the wooden floor. Then he painted them to look like tiles.

Use crayons or colored pencils to make some patterns that Grant Wood would enjoy.

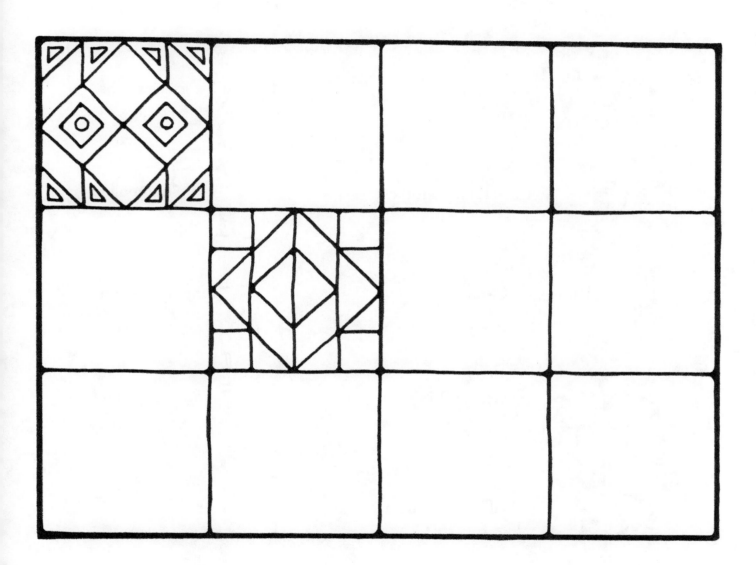

IOWA INVENTORS

Inventions happen when someone notices a problem and finds a way to solve it. Many inventive people are from Iowa, including the people whose inventions are shown below.

Can you match the name of each invention with the name of its inventor? Use the picture clues to help you.

John Froelich		Eskimo Pie ice-cream bar
Wallace Hume Carothers		trampoline
Christian Nelson		vending machine
George P. Nissen		merry-go-round
Willhelm Schneider		nylon
F.A. Wittern		gasoline tractor

President Hoover

President Herbert Hoover, who lived from 1874 to 1964, was born in West Branch. First, he was a mining engineer. Later, he helped people in Europe rebuild their lives after World War I. After that, he worked for the U.S. government. Finally, he was elected president in 1929. His home in West Branch is now a museum.

Which president was he? Color each space that has a dot in it and find out.

NANCY DREW BEGAN IN IOWA

Nancy Drew is a girl detective in stories written more than sixty years ago by Mildred Wirt Benson. Benson was born in Ladora. When the stories first appeared, Nancy Drew was a very popular character. Nancy Drew books are still sold today, bringing the total sold to more than eighty million.

Oh, no! Nancy's diary is missing. Can you help her find it?

CIRCUS TIME

The Ringling Brothers Circus began in McGregor. Three of the Ringling brothers were born in Iowa. This circus has toured throughout the United States and Europe for many years. In 1907, the Ringling brothers bought the Barnum and Bailey Circus, which was called "The Greatest Show on Earth."

Color the circus clowns on this page. Then draw and color some of your own.

Famous Architect in Iowa

Frank Lloyd Wright, one of the United States' greatest architects, designed ten houses in Iowa. Cedar Rock, or the Lowell Walter House, was built in the 1950s. It is near Quasqueton, on a bluff overlooking the Wapsipinicon River. Wright put his signature on a tile at the home's entrance.

Pretend that you are an architect. See if you can design three different home entrances. Color them the way they would look best.

BUFFALO BILL CODY

William Cody was born just outside LeClaire. First, he worked as a Pony Express rider. Then, he was a scout for the U.S. Army during the Civil War. He became Buffalo Bill when he won a buffalo-shooting competition. He wanted people to know what the West was like, so he created his Wild West show. He traveled with it throughout Europe and the United States for more than twenty years.

Can you connect the dots to draw the wild animal hidden below?
Be careful and don't get too close. This animal can be dangerous.

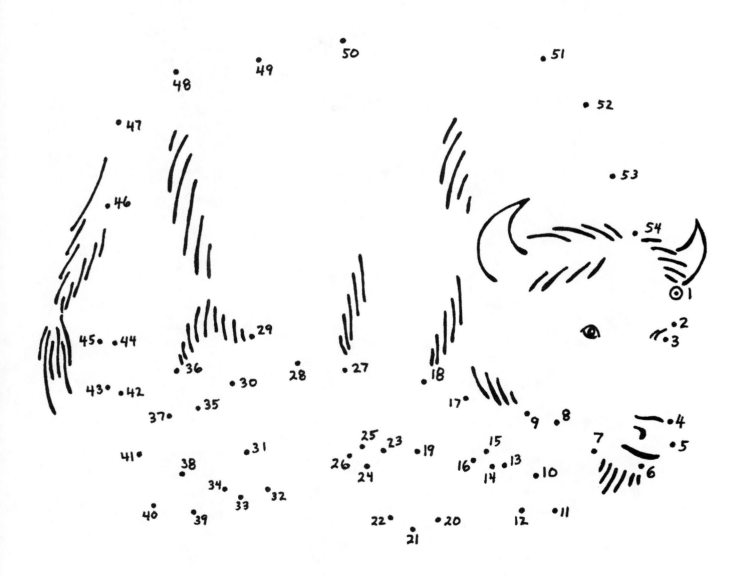

IT GROWS IN IOWA

It is yellow and wrapped in green. Connect the dots
and complete the sentence to find out what it is.

Iowa is the land where the tall _____ grows.

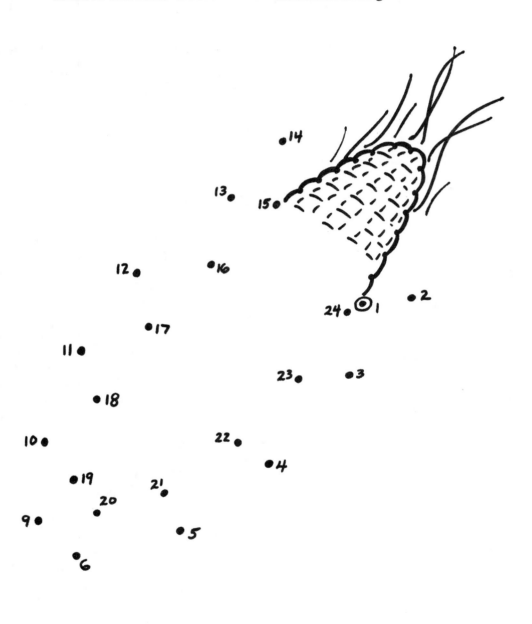

Iowa Agriculture

Iowa helps feed the rest of the United States—and the world, too. Iowa produces important crops and livestock. Iowa farms grow more of some kinds of food than most other states do.

Fill in each blank in these sentences about food production. Use the picture clues to help you. You might be surprised by what you find!

eighth

Of the fifty states, Iowa ranks _____ in raising sheep.

tenth

Iowa ranks _____ in the nation in turkey farming.

first

In egg production, Iowa ranks _____ .

eighth

Iowa is _____ in the production of corn and soybeans.

tenth

Of all states in the nation, Iowa ranks _____ in cattle.

Iowa farmers rank _____ in raising pigs.

first

Farm Machinery

Use the picture alphabet code below to spell the names of machines used on Iowa farms.

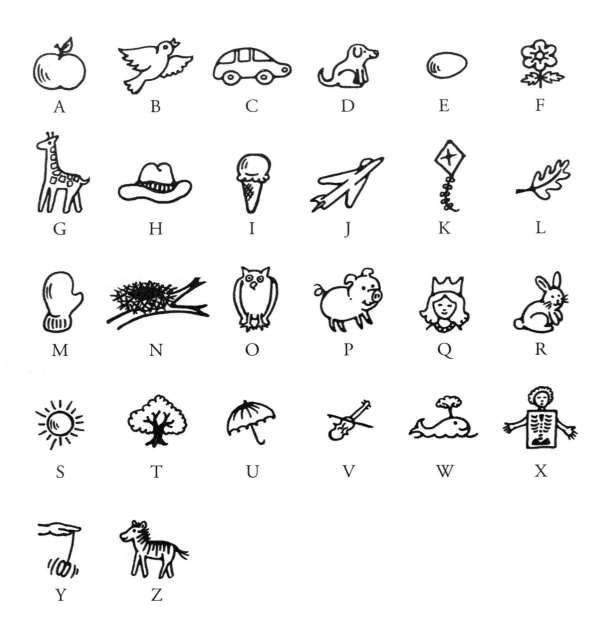

Fun at the State Fair

The Iowa State Fair is held each year in August. The state fair grounds are
in Des Moines, and the fair is one of the best in the nation. At the
fair, people display their finest products, livestock, and talent.

In 1941, the main event at the fair was the National Tall Corn Contest.
The winner was a cornstalk that was more than 23 feet tall.

What would you like to display at the fair? Draw a picture of it!

FARM ANIMALS

In the word search below, find some Iowa farm animals. They include the ostrich, cow, dog, chicken, mouse, horse, llama, pig, duck, cat, turkey, and sheep.

Look across, down, and at an angle to find the words.

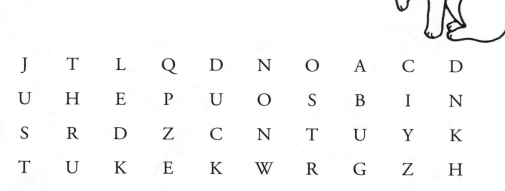

C T J T L Q D N O A C D

A E U H E P U O S B I N

T Q S R D Z C N T U Y K

Z S T U K E K W R G Z H

S C Q Q O E G L I P I G

C H A L D M Y R C M S M

D O E O Q L O Y H N C O

G O W E Q L H X T U P U

X S G P P A R O W F P S

Z D X F C M F Q R P A E

V P K K X A L L P S H D

A S W C H I C K E N E W

Roaring Excitement

The National Sprint Car Hall of Fame and Museum was opened in 1991, just off the Knoxville Raceway's second turn. The museum shows the amazing history of sprint car racing, including the development of open-wheel racing. It is the only sprint car racing museum in the United States.

There is sprint car hidden in the picture below.
Color the shapes that have a number to find the car.

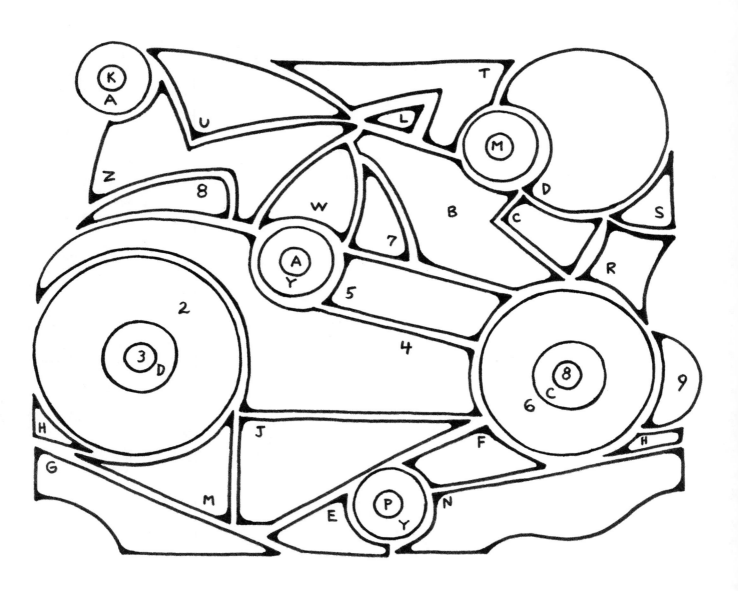

Railroads Great and Small

People who love trains should visit Trainland U.S.A. in Colfax. This museum is full of working toy trains. The museum tells about the development of railroads across the United States. It also has full-size trains and a 1928 Rock Island passenger car.

In the picture below, draw the rest of the train. You might also want to color it and draw the place it is passing through.

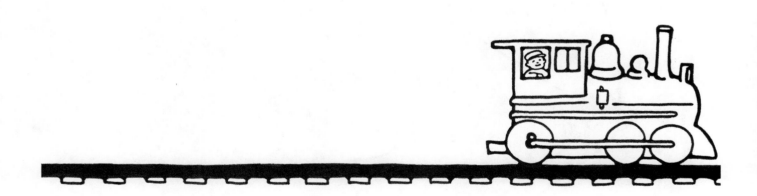

FIELD OF DREAMS

Have you ever wanted to catch your dreams or be a movie star? At Dyersville, you can play ball and look at the site of the famous movie, *Field of Dreams*.

Dream up the rest of this baseball diamond and cornfield.
Use your imagination—it's your field now!

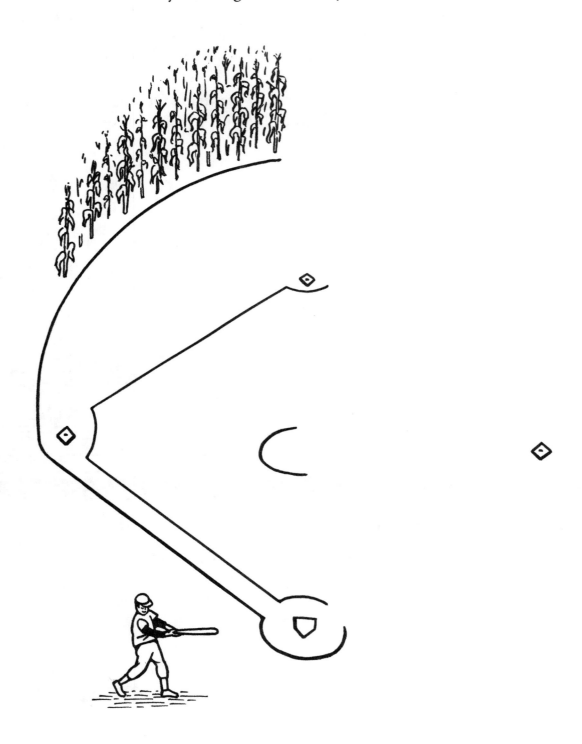

UP, UP, AND AWAY

What's in the air? Lots! Each summer, festivals in Storm Lake, Amana, Indianola, and Creston have hot-air balloons flying. And year-round, the Iowa Aviation and Preservation Center in Greenfield has aircraft from Iowa's aviation history. The center displays World War II aircraft, man-sized gliders, Tiger Moth biplanes, and a recent A-7 attack bomber from the Iowa Air National Guard.

Color these hot-air balloons and planes.

TOYS FROM ERTL®

Racing Champions Ertl, a toy company in Dyersville, manufactures almost all of the world's farm toys. These products gave the title "The Farm Toy Capital of the World" to this busy town.

Connect the dots to see one of the farm toys that this company makes.

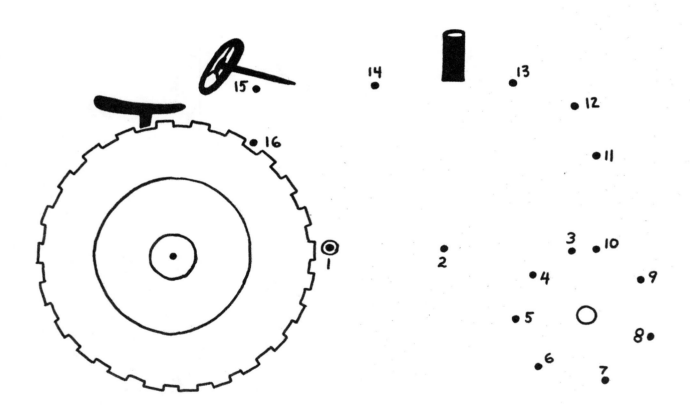

Cereal from Cedar Rapids

The Quaker Oats cereal factory in Cedar Rapids is one of the largest cereal plants in the world. It produces many foods with a picture of a Quaker man on them. This symbol stands for quality, purity, and honesty.

If you were a box designer for a cereal company, what kind of pictures would you put on your cereal boxes? Try your designs on the four boxes below.

Muscatine's Pearl Buttons

Muscatine once had the world's largest factory for making pearl buttons. These buttons were made from the shells of clams that grew in the Mississippi River. Once plastic buttons were invented, the need for clamshells vanished. Then the pearl button factories closed.

Look carefully at the buttons below. Can you draw lines to match up buttons that are exact opposites of each other?

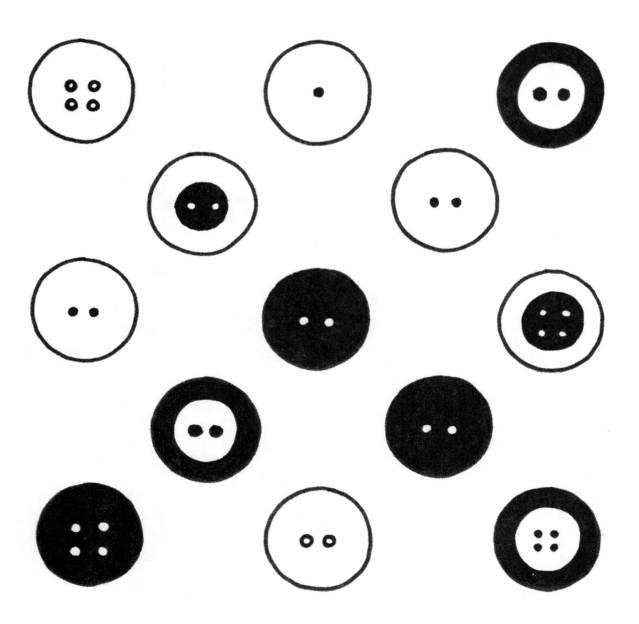

Snake Alley
Historic District

Snake Alley, known as the crookedest street in the world, goes for five half turns and two quarter turns through a historic neighborhood in Burlington. It was built in 1894 as a shortcut down the bluffs to the town's center.

Can you find your way down Snake Alley?

Amish Country

Many Old Order Amish people settled in the Kalona area. Old Order Amish people live without telephones, electric light, cars, jewelry, and buttons. They live differently from most people because of religious beliefs from hundreds of years ago. Today, the Amish women make beautiful quilts. Some people call Kalona the quilt capital of Iowa.

Use crayons or colored pencils to color the quilt.
The color key helps you create an Amish star design.

P - purple   B - blue   X - black   G - green

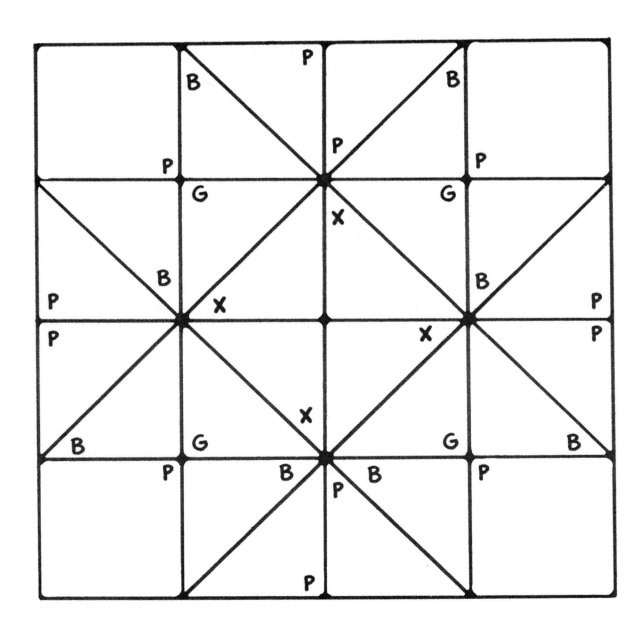

From Czechoslovakia

For years and years, many people who lived in Cedar Rapids came from Czechoslovakia, a country in Central Europe. Many others had parents or grandparents from that country. In 1995, the National Czech and Slovak Museum opened in Cedar Rapids. The museum tells the story of the Czech and Slovak people, and it has an excellent costume exhibit.

Color the costumes using the code. You can make them as bright and beautiful as they are in the museum.

1 - red   2 - blue   3 - yellow   4 - green   5 - black

A Danish Community

Elk Horn is the center of the largest Danish settlement in the United States. In the town is a structure that was built in Denmark. The structure was moved in pieces to its new home in Elk Horn.

Connect the dots to learn what that structure is.
It is still being used to grind wheat into flour today.

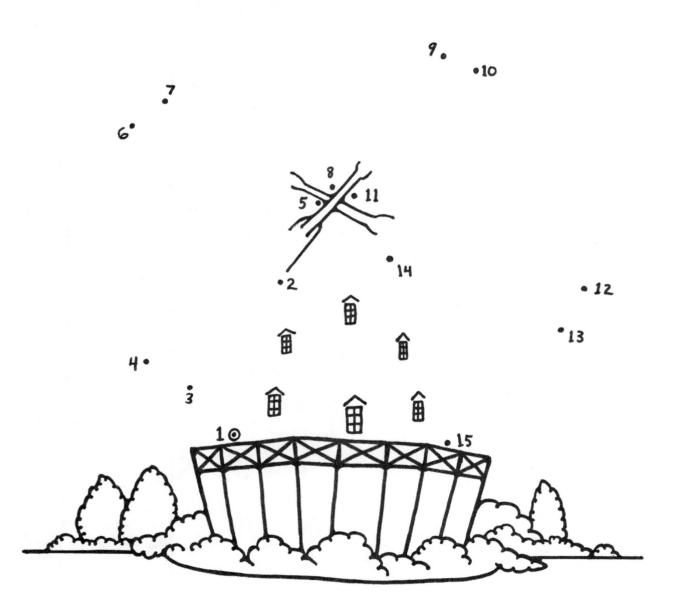

VESTERHEIM

More than a hundred years ago, Iowa's Norwegian immigrants called Iowa *Vesterheim*, their new western home. Today, the Vesterheim Norwegian-American Museum in Decorah displays objects from long-ago homes. These include toys, tools, and costumes. The museum takes up fifteen historic buildings. It is the largest museum in the United States for an immigrant group.

Rosemaling is a traditional Norwegian craft. It is carved or painted decorations that use flower designs. This rosemaling design needs some color. Use the colors you like to finish it.

Amana Colonies

The Amana colonies are a group of seven villages that were first settled by German craft workers and scholars. Today, these villages are a National Historic Landmark. They bring many visitors to Iowa.

Unscramble the words to spell the names of all seven villages.

THOUS AANMA

_____

DMEDIL ANAMA

_____

SETA MANAA

_____

MAANA

_____

ESMHTDAEO

_____

GHIH NAAMA

_____

SETW NAMAA

_____

The Meskwaki

The Meskwaki group of Native Americans is also known as the Sac and Fox of the Mississippi. They currently own more than seven thousand acres of land in central Iowa near Tama. They call their land a settlement, which means that the people own the land together. No family owns any land by itself. The women and girls of this group specialize in beautiful beadwork.

Color the pattern below with the colors in the key. You will see a real Native American design that is used in Meskwaki beadwork.

1 - blue   2 - red   3 - orange   4 - yellow

Iowa's Trees

Eleven kinds of trees are often found in Iowa's bottomland forests. Bottomlands are low-lying areas near rivers and streams. Bottomland trees are the elderberry, box elder, hackberry, chokecherry, sycamore, black walnut, willow, river birch, silver maple, green ash, and cottonwood.

Can you label each bottomland leaf with its name? The first letter of each name is given to help you. You can also color the leaves.

g __ __ __ __   __ __ __

b __ __   __ __ __ __ __

h __ __ __ __ __ __ __ __ __

s __ __ __ __ __ __ __ __ __

e _ _ _ _ _ _ _ _ _ _

w _ _ _ _ _

r _ _ _ _ _ _ _ _

c _ _ _ _ _ _ _ _ _ _

s _ _ _ _ _ _ _

c _ _ _ _ _ _ _

b _ _ _ _ _ _ _ _ _

Loess Hills

The Loess Hills are a land formation that is found only one other place in the world—China. Loess is very fine soil that was blown in by the wind long ago. *Loess* is pronounced "less." The Missouri River is on one side of the Loess Hills, and the rest of Iowa is on the other. If you are traveling in western Iowa, you can follow the Scenic Byway signs to the Loess Hills.

Can you help the children get to the Missouri River?
Be careful—don't get lost in the prairie grass.

CRYSTAL LAKE CAVE

Just south of Dubuque is a wonderful cave. It is Iowa's largest cave.
One of its most beautiful rooms is called The Chapel. This room
is small, and its walls are covered with glittering crystals.

Other rooms have rock formations caused by dripping water. The rooms have stalactites—
formations that hang from the ceiling. They also have stalagmites—formations that rise from
the floor. Sometimes these two formations meet in midair and become columns.

Some caves have bats in them. How many bats can you find in this cave?

IOWA WILDLIFE

Several kinds of wild animals belong to the lands of Iowa. Use the picture alphabet code below to find which animals match the coded words.

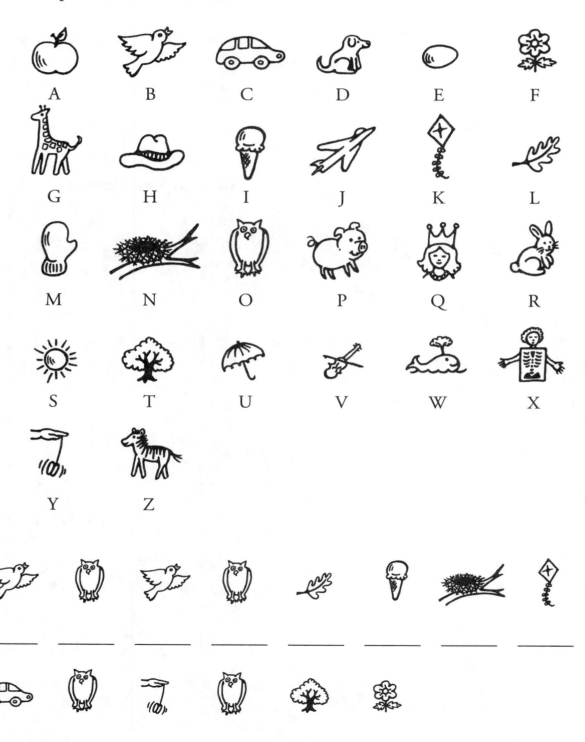

AN IoWa FiSHMarKet

The Mississippi River borders Iowa on the east. Many kinds of fish and edible water creatures live in the river. The best way to see them is to go to an early morning fishmarket at the river, and look at what has been caught.

Unscramble the letters by each picture to spell the name of each creature.

lee

— — —

figshar

— — — — — — —

parc

— — — —

belhudal

— — — — — — — —

geostnur

— — — — — — — —

lenchan schifat

— — — — — — — — — — — — —

papginns rutlet

— — — — — — — — — — — — —

EFFIGY MOUNDS

Long, long ago, Native Americans built mounds in many places in what is now the United States. Mounds are hills made of soil and rocks. In what is now Iowa and nearby states, people made special mounds called effigies. These mounds are shaped like animals! Some of them are hundreds of feet wide but only a few feet tall.

Color the spaces that have a dot in them to see the shapes of some of these special mounds. Can you find birds and bears?

Victorian Houses

Many styles of buildings are found in the cities and countryside of Iowa. A very fancy building style that people used more than a hundred years ago is called Victorian, after England's Queen Victoria. This style has very detailed woodwork and lots of decorations.

Look at the Victorian house below. Parts of the house are missing. Can you fill them in?

Iowa's Covered Bridges

About 12 miles from Winterset in Madison County, there are six covered bridges. There once were nineteen of them in the area. The bridge covers were made to protect the large, expensive floor timbers. The Roseman covered bridge was used as the setting for a recent movie, *The Bridges of Madison County*.

Help! The bridge is lost. Use a blue crayon to color the shapes with a letter. Then use a green crayon to color the shapes with a number. Now you can find the bridge.

Wooden Shoes and Tulips

Pella and Orange City were settled by Dutch immigrants. People celebrate their Dutch heritage each May with a Tulip Festival. Tulips were grown by the Dutch in the Netherlands before they came to the United States. During the festival, the tulips are in bloom all over town and people wear Dutch costumes, including wooden shoes.

This Dutch girl has lost one of her wooden shoes. Can you help her find it?

HIGHLANDERS

The University of Iowa's Scottish Highlander Bagpipe Band is the only one at a Big Ten school. This band's pipes and drums and Stewart plaid kilts have entertained crowds at football games for the past forty-five years. Once, this group was the only all-woman bagpipe band in the world. Today, it has both men and women as pipers.

Connect the dots to see the details of the Highlander's instrument and costume.

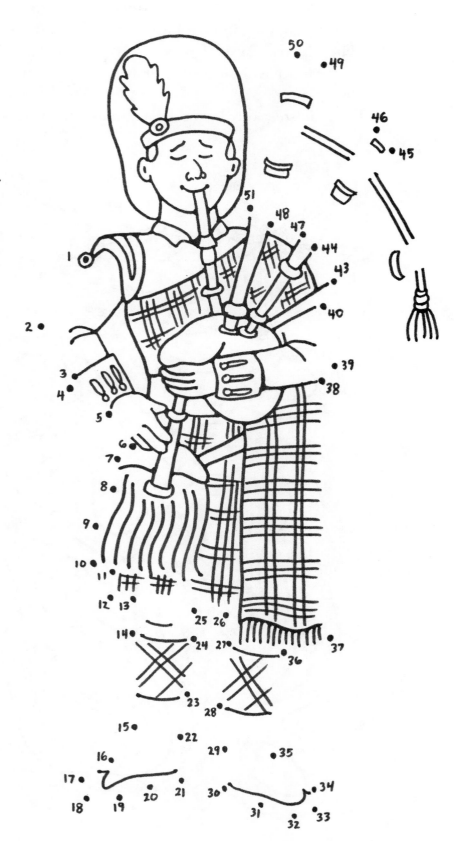

DRAGON BOATS

Each year, dragon boat races are held on the Cedar River in Cedar Rapids.
They are part of the Freedom Festival celebration around the Fourth of July.
These races have teams of racers who come from all over the world to compete.

Can you steer the dragon boat through the maze to the flag at the finish line?

RAGBRAI

RAGBRAI, or the Register's Annual Great Bike Ride Across Iowa, is one of the largest bike trips in the United States. It happens each year and is sponsored by a newspaper, the *Des Moines Register*. The cyclists cross Iowa, from the Missouri River to the Mississippi River. They ride for a week and go almost 500 miles. Can you find seven things wrong with this picture of RAGBRAI?

Fun and Festivals

Iowa festivals celebrate state history with good food and fun times. They help people remember special events, special times of the year, or a person who has done something important.

Find some Iowa festival names hidden across and down in this puzzle. The festival names are Hoover Fest, Tulip, Nordic Fest, Oktoberfest, RAGBRAI, Julefest, Czech Days, and Hobo Days.

S	H	J	U	L	E	F	E	S	T	O
N	O	R	D	I	C	F	E	S	T	K
A	O	P	F	H	I	L	N	R	R	T
K	V	O	E	O	F	G	T	A	E	O
E	E	W	S	B	A	O	I	G	A	B
A	R	W	T	O	I	O	M	B	T	E
L	F	O	I	D	R	D	E	R	S	R
L	E	W	V	A	X	L	S	A	L	F
E	S	A	E	Y	T	U	L	I	P	E
Y	T	M	E	S	K	W	A	K	I	S
H	C	Z	E	C	H	D	A	Y	S	T

FORT ATKINSON

Fort Atkinson was built in Winneshiek County. It is the only U.S. fort ever built to protect one group of Native Americans, the Winnebago, from other Native American groups and from white settlers.

Color this drawing of the fort by following the key.

1 - blue   2 - green   3 - yellow   4 - black   5 - brown   6 - tan

ESCAPING SLAVERY

The Underground Railroad had paths throughout Iowa. This "railroad" was a network of homes for runaway slaves to hide in while they tried to escape from the southern states to Canada.

Can you help the slave move through Iowa on his way to Canada and freedom?

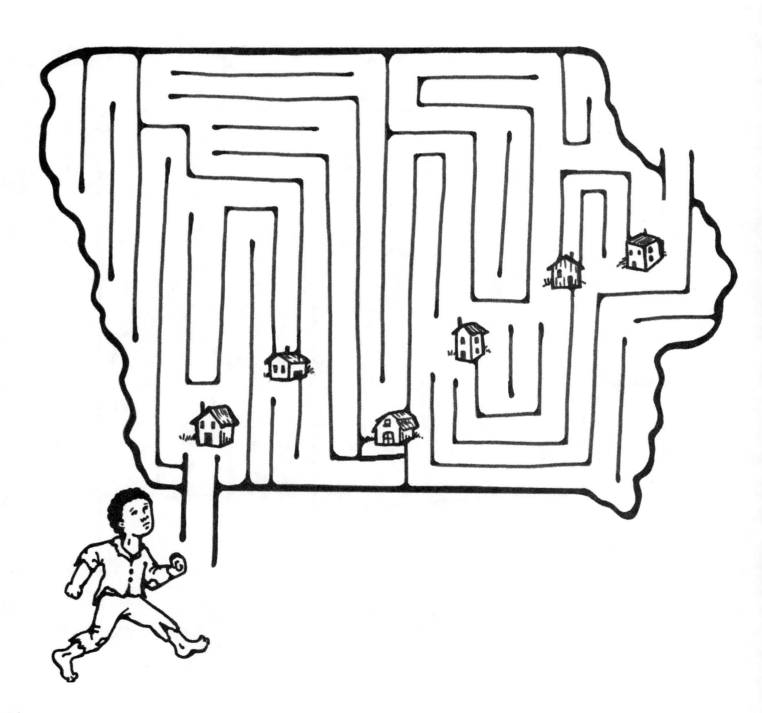

The Explorers

Meriwether Lewis and William Clark were chosen by President Thomas Jefferson to explore the land that the United States bought from France in 1803. This land was called the Louisiana Purchase. The men traveled up the Missouri River along the western side of what is now Iowa.

Connect the dots. You will see a boat like the keelboat that Lewis and Clark used for their travels.

IOWA HISTORY

Across
1. Region made of soil brought to western Iowa by wind during the Ice Ages
2. The _____ War was a battle in 1832 between the United States and the Sac and Fox Native Americans.
3. This "railroad" helped free slaves who passed through Iowa.

Down
1. Iowa was part of this land deal with France in 1803.
2. A trail from Illinois to Utah used by a religious group
3. Seven colonies settled by a religious group from Germany. Now a National Historic Landmark

Hints
Louisiana Purchase
Amana Colonies
Underground Railroad
Mormon Trail
Loess Hills
Blackhawk

Abbie Gardner's Home

The cabin where Abbie Gardner and her family lived in 1856 is located in the beautiful Lakes Region of northwest Iowa. The cabin is a reminder of one of the most famous events of Iowa history. When you visit the cabin, you learn the dramatic story of Abbie Gardner and the Dakota Native American leader, Inkpadutah.

Look at the cabins below. Can you circle the two that look exactly alike?

ANSWER KEY

Page 2:

State flag

Wild rose

Geode

Great seal

Oak

Eastern
goldfinch

Page 3:

15 IOWAs

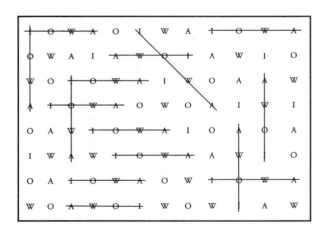

Page 4:

6 - Des Moines
8 - Cedar Rapids
3 - Davenport
10 - Sioux City
5 - Waterloo

1 - Iowa City
7 - Dubuque
2 - Council Bluffs
9 - Ames
4 - Cedar Falls

Page 5:

Page 6:

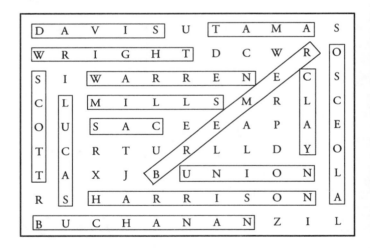

Page 7:

Page 9:

It's a trombone! So the song title is "76 Trombones."

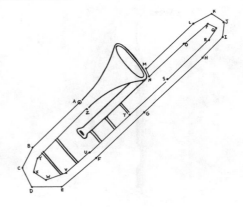

Page 10:

Page 12:

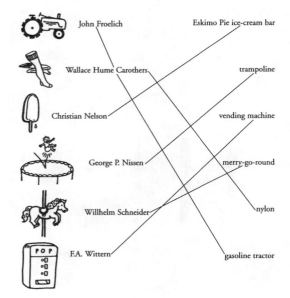

Page 13:

thirty-first president

Page 14:

Page 17:

It's a buffalo!

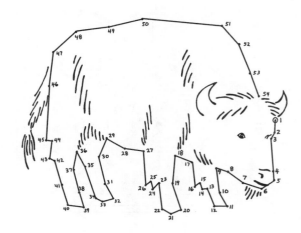

Page 18:

corn

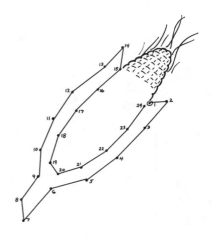

Page 19:

tenth in sheep raising; tenth in turkey farming; eighth in egg production; first in corn and soybean production; eighth in cattle; first in pig raising

Page 21:

tractor, combine, baler, spreader, disc, wagon, harvester, plow

Page 23:

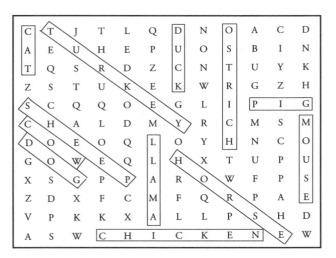

Page 24:

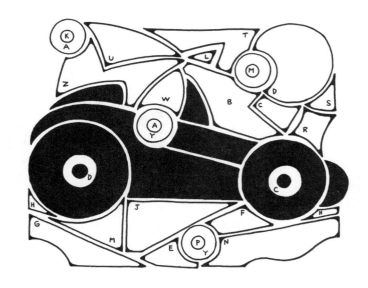

Page 28:

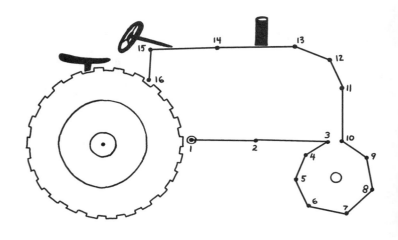

Page 30:

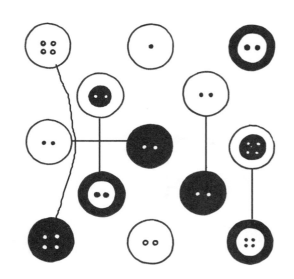

Page 31:

Page 34:

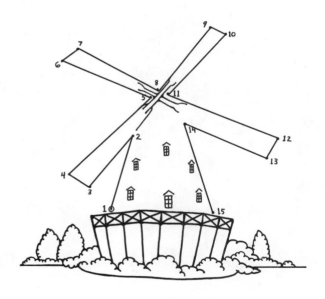

Page 36:

SOUTH AMANA, MIDDLE AMANA, EAST AMANA, AMANA, HOMESTEAD, HIGH AMANA, WEST AMANA

Pages 38, 39:

green ash, box elder, hackberry, sycamore, elderberry, willow, river birch, chokecherry, silver maple, cottonwood, black walnut

Page 40:

Page 41:

11 bats

Pages 42, 43:

bobolink, coyote, monarch butterfly, garter snake, American toad, buffalo

Page 44:

eel, garfish, carp, bullhead, sturgeon, channel catfish, snapping turtle

Page 45:

Page 46:

Page 47:

Page 48:

Page 49:

Page 50:

Page 51:

Page 52:

S	H	J	U	L	E	F	E	S	T	O
N	O	R	D	I	C	F	E	S	T	K
A	P	F	H	I	L	N	R	R	T	T
K	V	O	O	F	G	T	E	E	O	O
E	E	S	B	A	O	I	G	A	B	B
A	W	T	O	I	O	M	B	T	E	E
L	F	O	I	R	D	E	R	S	R	R
L	O	W	D	X	L	S	A	L	F	F
E	W	V	A	Y	T	U	L	I	P	E
Y	S	A	Y	S	K	W	A	K	I	S
H	T	M	E	S	K	W	A	K	I	T
	C	Z	E	C	H	D	A	Y	S	

JULEFEST · NORDICFEST · HOBODAYS · TULIP · CZECHDAYS · OKTOBERFEST

Page 54:

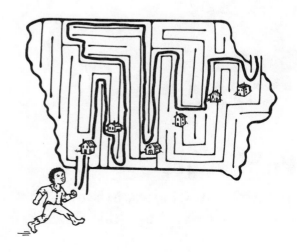

Page 55:

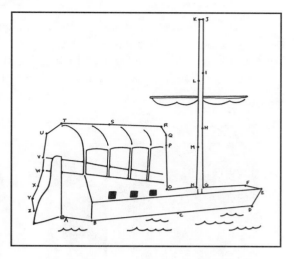

Page 56:

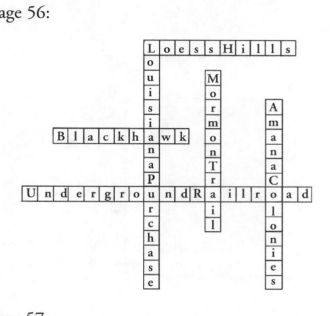

Loess Hills · Louisiana Purchase · Mormon Trail · Amana Colonies · Blackhawk · Underground Railroad

Page 57:

Take Off with the *Alpha Flight Books* Series!

Here's a series of hardcover jacketed ABC books that teach children the alphabet while also giving them interesting information about each letter's topic. The series is designed for the preschool and beginning reader, but its format and fun facts make it suitable for ages 4 through 8. Each letter of the alphabet has a two-page spread consisting of:
• the letter in both upper and lower case   • a three- to four-sentence explanation of each letter's topic
• a photograph   • illustrations

"C" is for California
1892920271 • $17.95

"C" is for Canada
1892920301 • $17.95

"M" is for Missouri
1892920263 • $17.95

**"M" is for Missouri's
Rocks and Minerals**
1892920298 • $17.95

"T" is for Texas
189292028X • $17.95

"F" is for Firefighting
1892920204 • $17.95

"I" is for Illinois
1892920417 • $17.95

"M" is for Massachusetts
1892920425 • $17.95

"M" is for Michigan
1892920433 • $17.95

"N" is for New York
1892920441 • $17.95

GHB Publishers

3906 Old Highway 94 South, Suite 300 / St. Charles, Missouri 63304
888-883-4427 / FAX: 636-441-7941 / www.ghbpublishers.com